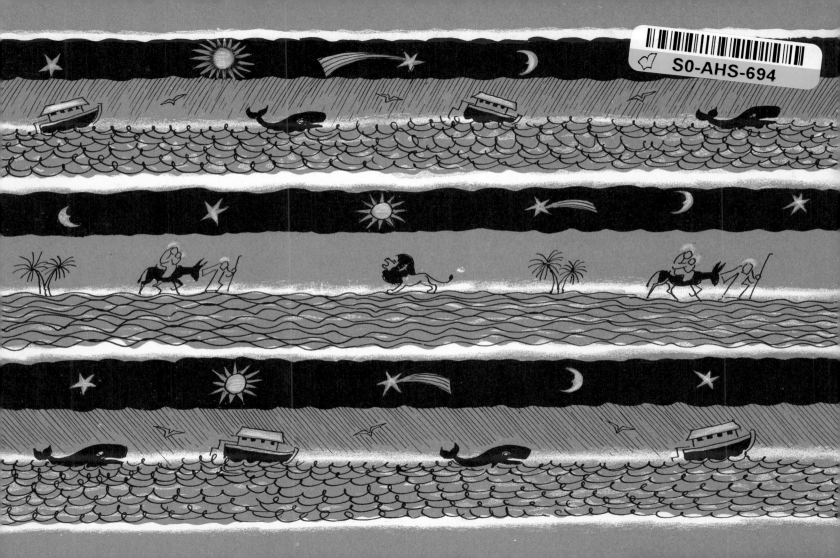

THE PEACEABLE KINGDOM

AND OTHER POEMS BY
ELIZABETH COATSWORTH

ILLUSTRATIONS BY
FRITZ EICHENBERG

PANTHEON BOOKS

FOR MEG WITH MY LOVE

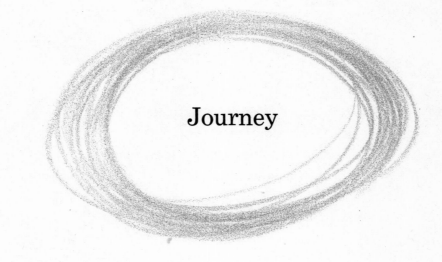

Journey

"It's a long way over the mountains,
it's a long, long way to the Ark,"
said the little lion to the great big lion,
"Can we get there by dark?"

And the mountain sheep and the coneys
and the eagles with pale fixed eyes
and the quick gazelles all answered,
"Tonight the moon will rise.

"We shall travel over the mountains
among the boulders and rocks,
your golden father shall lead us,
we will ask advice from the fox.

"We shall travel by sunlight and moonlight
and when they set, through the dark—
it's a long way over the mountains,
but at last we shall reach the Ark."

"It's a long, long way through the desert
and why should we fear the rain?"
said the little camel to the great big camel,
"I want to go home again!"

"We have to go on," said the lizards
and the jackals which live by the springs,
"And we must go on," cried the falcons,
spreading their shadowy wings.

"We must travel through heat and windstorm,
we must pass over burning sand,
for the doors of the Ark stand open
in a far-off and chosen land."

"It's a very long march through the forest
and the Ark is far, far away,"
said the little elephant to the great big elephant,
as the blue of the sky turned gray.

"Oh, it's going to rain!" snarled the tigers,
"and you know how we hate the rain!"
And the cobras said, and the cockatoos,
"Some day we'll come home again.

"Some day we'll return to the jungle,
and the moose will return to their trees,
with the fallow deer and the porcupines
and the squirrels and chickadees."

"It's a very hard run through the grasses
and I'm tired enough to drop,"
said the little giraffe to the great tall giraffe,
"At least for a minute, let's stop."

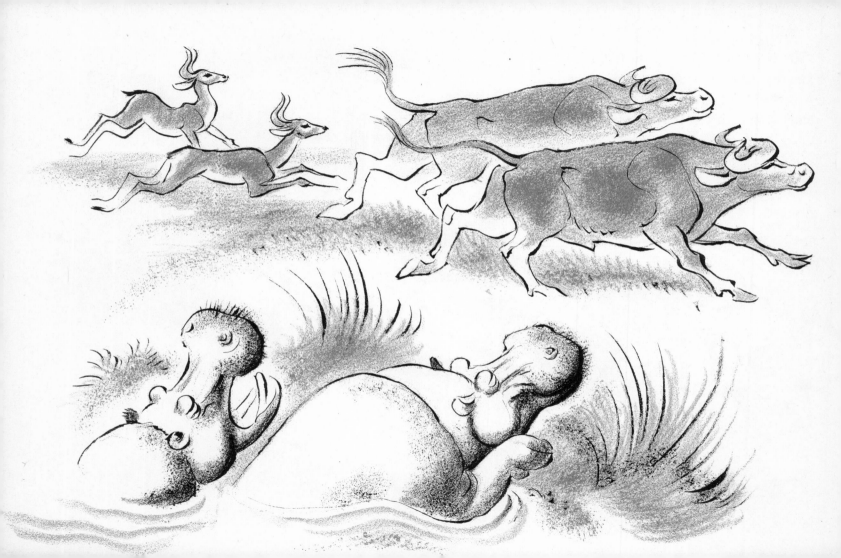

But the hartebeest and the buffalo,
hippopotami, zebras and all,
kept on, and they said as they hurried,
"We have heard a wonderful call,

"A voice spoke over the prairie,
and a voice called over the plain,
and it told us to come and come quickly
before the terrible rain."

"It's a long, long road we're going
and I don't know why we go,"
whined the puppy dog to the great big dog
dragging his feet so slow.

But the cats replied and the horses,
the cattle and donkeys said,
"It's a better thing to be tired—
dog-tired—than being dead!

"We must travel this road, long and weary,
we must swim across many a stream
and all for a warning which sounded
like a voice which speaks in a dream.

"But the rooster has heard, and the turkeys,
the pigs have answered that call.
We must go to the Ark which awaits us,
To shelter us, one and all."

And the sky grew blacker and blacker
and the winds began to howl,
and the lightning snapped like an angry whip
and deep was the thunder's growl.

And the birds of the air all hurried,
and the animals ran their best,
and the lizards and frogs and the serpents
somehow kept up with the rest.

And into the wide, wide doorway
they tumbled their way, pell-mell,
while the riven storm clouds opened
and the first fierce raindrops fell.

And the animals sighed with contentment
as outside the world grew dark
and they sang, "How far we have journeyed,
but at last we are safe in the Ark!"

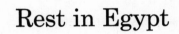

Rest in Egypt

from a medieval legend

Weary were the wanderers
weary of their flight,
said the lady faintly,
"I can do no more."
The tired donkey halted,
and, listening, they heard
far-off and terrible
a lion roar.

Hot was the sun,
yellow was the sand,
not a green tree cast its shade
across the bitter road.
"Death though it may mean,
I must rest," she said,
and gently Joseph lifted down
the donkey's load.

He spread his cloak beside a rock
where a coolness fell,
the baby wakened in her arms,
touched her cheek and smiled,
nearby a spring appeared,
and soon a breeze arose
eager to comfort
mother and child.

Now came the creatures
who lived in the desert,
the lion and the lioness
walking side by side,
and the fearless baby
reached his hand to touch them,
laid it on that flowing mane,
that sun-bright hide.

"You shall be the king of beasts,
and you shall be the queen,"
kindly said the lady,
"Since you know his worth.
While King Herod hunts us
with his sworded men,
you alone bear witness
to his birth."

Then came the jackals
bowing down their heads,
and the little foxes,
dwellers of the waste.
The tall soft-foot camels
knelt before the child,
and the ostriches ran up
in their haste.

Next came the lesser birds,
the eagles and the hawks
and the buzzards dropping
out of the still air;
with them came the river birds,
flocks of ducks and cranes,
and the blue kingfishers,
pair by pair.

Last came the reptiles,
beetles, black and horny,
lizards and hop-toads,
frogs, great and small.
While the lady thanked them
to the humblest buzz-fly,
her son gave them his blessing,
each and all.

There on Joseph's cloak
sat enthroned the mother
and in her two arms
held the new-born king.
Strange were the courtiers
who came to pay their homage,
but beautiful was the light of joy
shining on everything!

The Peaceable Kingdom

When the lion lies down with the lamb
and the Peaceable Kingdom is come
you may go in your little white dress
into the forest alone.

You may eat of the fruit of all trees
and drink of the springs at their roots,
stones will not cut you, nor bruise,
so away with your little white boots!

Barefoot, with flying hair,
you may walk wherever you please,
brushed only by flowers and ferns,
protected by fostering trees.

The gentle clouds of the birds
will follow close by your head,
and the panther walk by your side
with soft and sinewy tread.

The owl will come at your call,
the snake will bracelet your arm,
you shall sleep in the cave of the bear
and come to no harm.

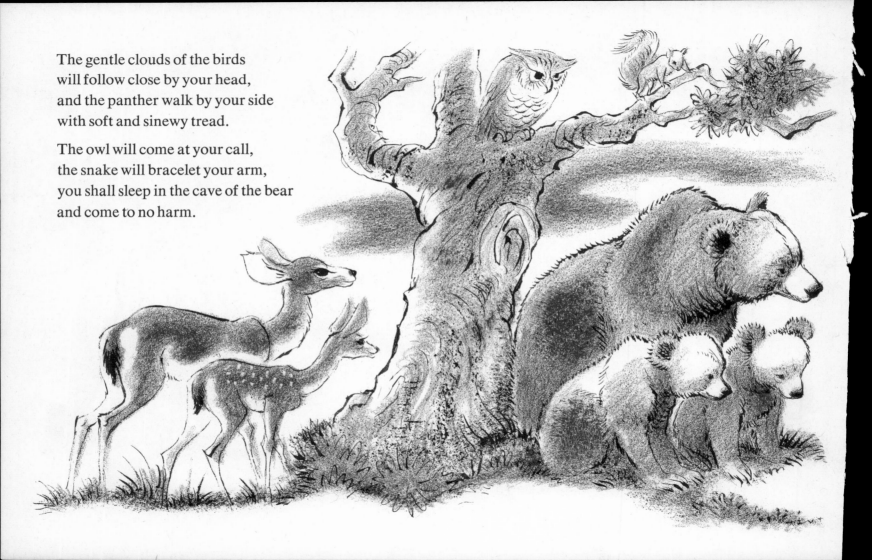

And when you are hungry, the bees
will show where their honey is stored,
and the squirrels will bring you the nuts
from their hollow-tree hoard.

Nor shall you lack for old friends
for the ox will quit his dark stall,
and the horse will lend you his speed
and the mastiff come to your call.

The cat, too, will play at your feet—
oh, merry the cat in that hour!—
on your shoulder a kitten shall ride
like a nodding flower.

All things will turn harmless and gay,
the wind will not bring with it cold,
and the innocent lightnings will play
in a startle of gold,

While the thunder beats on its drum
to which the butterflies dance
till the sun shall shine forth, and the storm
be gone, like a trance.

Then at last, when the shadows grow long,
barefoot, with flying hair,
in your little white dress you may stand
with remembering stare.

But you cannot be lost, for all paths
shall lead you back to your home,
when the lion lies down with the lamb
and the Peaceable Kingdom is come.